Where's Jesus?

Jesus heals a lame man: Mark 2:1-12

Jesus calms the storm: Mark 4:35-41

Jesus feeds five thousand people: Mark 6:30-44

Jesus heals a blind man: Mark 8:22-26

Jesus heals ten men of a skin disease: Luke 17:11-19

Jesus blesses the children: Mark 10:13-16

Where's Jesus?

LOYOLAPRESS.
CHICAGO

Stephanie Jeffs and Sarah Beth Laver

Everywhere Jesus went something exciting happened.

Simeon and his mom hurried to Capernaum by the Sea of Galilee.

"Keep up, Simeon!" said Mom.
"We're going to find Jesus."

"Where's Jesus?" asked Simeon. "Is he here?"
"Yes," said an old man. "He is in that house."

The sea was very rough.
"Where's Jesus?" asked Simeon. "Is he here?"
"Yes," said a man with a net.
"He's gone out in that boat."

Simeon and his mom walked up the hill.
"Keep up, Simeon!" said Mom.
"We're going to find Jesus."

Simeon and his mom set off for Bethsaida.
"Keep up, Simeon!" said Mom.
"We're going to find Jesus."

It took some time to get there.
"Where's Jesus?" asked Simeon.
"Is he here?"
"Yes," said a young girl.
"He is in the town."

"Look!" said Simeon.
"Jesus has made a blind man see!"

It was a long way to Samaria.
"Keep up, Simeon!" said Mom.
"We're going to find Jesus!"
They came to a village and stopped at the well.

"Look!" said Simeon.
"Jesus has cured ten men
of a terrible skin disease!"

"Keep up, Simeon!" said Mom.
"We're going to find Jesus!"
"But who is Jesus?" asked Simeon.
He didn't want to go any farther.
"He's God's Son," said Mom.

"He healed a man who couldn't walk.

 He calmed a storm.

He fed a huge crowd of people with a boy's lunch.

 He made a blind man see.

He cured ten men of leprosy."

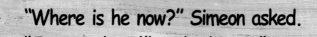

"Where is he now?" Simeon asked.
"Jesus is here!" said a big, tall man.
"And he wants the children to go to him!"

Now Simeon could do what he really wanted.
He could be with Jesus.

Published in North America by Loyola Press
3441 N. Ashland Ave.
Chicago, IL 60657
ISBN: 0-8294-1728-1

Published in the UK by Eagle Publishing
PO Box 530, Guildford, Surrey GU2 4FH

First North American edition 2002